This book belongs to

"The NSPCC is pleased to work with Egmont World on the development of this series of story books. We believe that they will help parents better understand their children's needs and help children cope with a variety of social issues."
Jim Harding, Chief Executive, NSPCC.

The NSPCC Happy Kids logo and Happy Kids characters:
TM & © NSPCC 2000. Licensed by CPL
NSPCC Registered Charity Number: 216401

Published in Great Britain by Egmont World Ltd.,
Deanway Technology Centre, Wilmslow Road, Handforth,
Cheshire, SK9 3FB. Printed in Italy
ISBN PBK 0 7498 4639 9
ISBN HBK 0 7498 4734 4
A catalogue record for this book is available from the British Library.

Emily

NSPCC happy kids

...and the stranger

Hi! I'm Emily and I'm one of the Happy Kids.

Written by **Michaela Morgan**
Illustrated by **Rob Lee**
Series Consultant **Wendy Cooling**
Happy Kids Created by **Richard Wetherill**

Emily is a happy kid.
She is funny, she is friendly and she is
a bit of a chatterbox.

All day long she chatters
… and shouts and sings

Emily is the loudest singer in her school.

When the teacher asks the children to sing
out loud and clear, she always says to Emily,

Not THAT loud and
clear, Emily! There's no
need to shout!

Emily will talk to anyone or anything.

Once she saw a little dog with a stick. Emily went up to the dog and took its stick. "I'll throw it for you," she said.

Do you know what the dog did?
It showed its teeth and snarled.

Emily's mum said,
"Most animals and
people are friendly,
but some will hurt you.
Promise never to go
up to strange animals
or people.

And never, ever, go off with someone without telling me. Remember what they told you at school."

I remember.

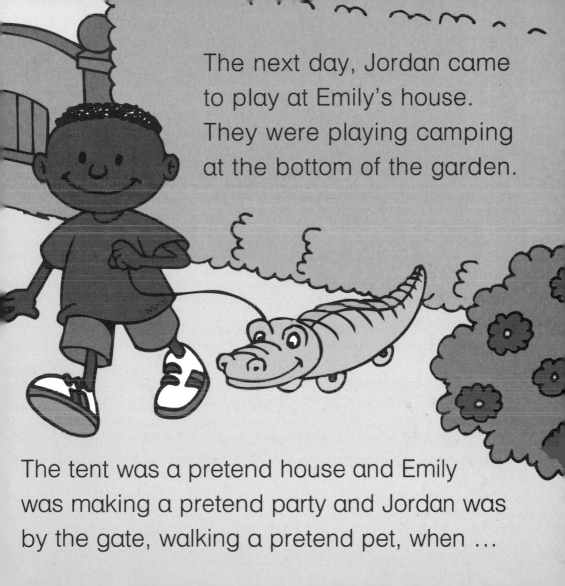

The next day, Jordan came
to play at Emily's house.
They were playing camping
at the bottom of the garden.

The tent was a pretend house and Emily
was making a pretend party and Jordan was
by the gate, walking a pretend pet, when …

"Hello," said a voice.
A man was leaning over the gate
eating an ice cream.

It was just the sort Jordan liked best!
The day before when he was at the shops
with his mum he had begged her
to buy him an ice cream.
"I'm just going down to the shop to
get another ice cream," the man said.
"Why don't you come along?"

Jordan went up to the gate, but just then Emily popped out of the tent.

"I didn't see you in there," said the man.
"You can come too!"
"My mum says I'm never to go off
with a stranger," said Emily.
"But I'm not a stranger," said the man.
"Jordan saw me yesterday in the shop."

"Come on. We have to hurry or
the shop will close."
The man opened the gate.
"Well … " said Emily.
"My mum will be very cross if I go
anywhere without telling her."
"She need never know," smiled the man.
"It can be our secret."

Emily thought for a little bit.
Then she took a big breath and …

in her very loudest voice she shouted ...

It was such a loud voice that it made Jordan jump.
It made the man run away. It made both their
mums come running out of
the kitchen.

they shouted.

Emily told them all about it.
"Isn't it naughty to shout at a grown-up?"
asked Jordan. "Isn't it bad to say no?"
"Did I do the right thing?" Emily asked.
She was a bit worried.
"You did exactly the right thing,"
said her mum.

"And I think you deserve a reward.
Let's all go together to get those ice creams."

Emily and Jordan and their mums went to the shop together.

On the way home they went through the park.
Jordan zoomed down the hill.
"YIPPEE!" he said in a loud voice.
Emily zoomed down the hill.
"YIPPEEE!" she said in a very loud voice.

EMILY — A STORY ABOUT KEEPING SAFE

Advice to Parents and Carers

As well as providing tales which will entertain children, this series of stories about the Happy Kids illustrates how we should treat and care for each other.

When your child has read the story or you have read it with him or her, you may wish to discuss the issues raised. Find a quiet place and be prepared to spend a little time together. Let your child ask any questions he or she likes arising from the story.

This story about Emily can be used as a basis for discussing how children can be kept safe from strangers who might harm them. Please reassure your children that they need not be worried by the story because Emily and Jordan were sensible and they came to no harm. Parents and carers can teach their children the following steps to take which can help keep them safe.

- Never go off with an adult you don't know. Never accept sweets or presents from them, however friendly they seem.
- Remember the three "W's". Never go out on your own without first telling the adult looking after you **where** you are going, **who** you are going with, and **when** you will be coming home.
- If someone you don't know tries to force you into a car or to do things you don't like, you should shout "NO!" as loudly as you can, kick and bite and do anything else to escape.
- A person is still a stranger, even if they happen to know your name.

If you want to talk through parenting issues of this sort you can phone Parentline on: 0808 800 2222 (Textphone: 0800 783 6783).

NSPCC
CHILD PROTECTION
HELPLINE
0800 800 500
TEXTPHONE 0800 056 0566

Special Offers for Happy Kids readers

Thank you for purchasing this NSPCC Happy Kids story book, which will automatically generate a contribution to the NSPCC cause, to help more children become happier children.

We've also got some special gift offers for Happy Kids readers.
This six-piece school set is available for only £2.50 and includes a pencil case, two pencils and a sharpener, an eraser and 15cm ruler – all items featuring the Happy Kids characters.

Simply send a cheque for only £2.50 (inc. post and package) to
NSPCC Happy Kids,
Marketing Department (6pcs),
Egmont World Ltd, PO Box 7,
Manchester MI9 2HD.
Please include your name and address including postcode and allow 28 days for delivery. We will then give 10p from the sale of each School Set to the NSPCC.

Thank you

We are the Happy Kids!